CGP

of

CREATIVE MINDS

Credits

Editors: Claire Boulter, Anna Hall, Paul Jordin, Holly Poynton, Rebecca Tate

Consultant: Rachel Clark

With thanks to Janet Berkeley, Judy Hornigold, Andy Park, Holly Poynton, Glenn Rogers, Lucy Towle and Karen Wells for the proofreading.

With thanks to Laura Jakubowski for the copyright research.

With thanks to John Kitching for the design work.

Published by CGP

ISBN: 978 1 84762 475 8

Printed by Elanders Ltd, Newcastle upon Tyne.

The chapters in this book are based on real people and real events. However, some situations and dialogue have been changed for dramatic purposes. Some minor characters have been invented; any similarity to a real person, living or dead, is purely coincidence.

Contents

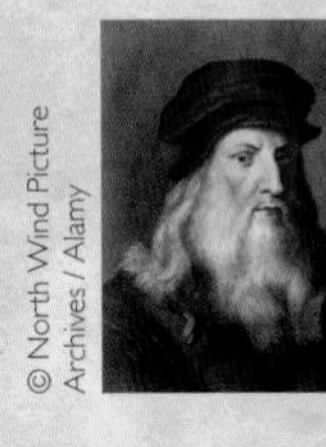

Leonardo da Vinci.. 1-13

Leonardo da Vinci (1452-1519) was an Italian painter, sculptor, engineer and inventor who created masterpieces such as the *Mona Lisa* and the *Last Supper*.

Wolfgang Amadeus Mozart..................14-26

Wolfgang Amadeus Mozart (1756-1791) was a child prodigy who played numerous musical instruments, performed in front of royalty and composed over 600 pieces.

Charles Dickens... 27-39

Charles Dickens (1812-1870) was a celebrated author who overcame poverty as a young boy to become one of the world's best-selling and most recognised writers.

Benjamin Zephaniah................................. 40-52

Benjamin Zephaniah (born 1958) left school at 13 unable to read and write. Since then, he has become an enormously successful poet and author.

Acknowledgements

Image on cover and introduction page reproduced by courtesy of Charles Dickens Museum London

Image on page 6 © De Agostini Picture Library / Studio AB / Bridgeman Images

Image of Leonardo da Vinci on back cover, contents page and page 8 © North Wind Picture Archives / Alamy

Image of Wolfgang Amadeus Mozart on back cover, contents page and page 21 © GL Archive / Alamy

Image on page 23: Marriage of Figaro poster by Tamcgath licenced for re-use under the Creative Commons licence http://creativecommons.org/licenses/by-sa/3.0/deed.en

Image on page 25 © University Library Salzburg, shelfmark G 992 II.

Image of Charles Dickens on back cover, contents page and page 34 © Heritage Image Partnership Ltd / Alamy

Image on page 37: Staplehurst rail crash Engraving in Illustrated London News 1865

Quote on page 40: "Dis Poetry" Benjamin Zephaniah, *City Psalms* (Bloodaxe Books 1992)

Quotes and book cover image on page 45: 26 words and the front cover in its entirety from TALKING TURKEYS by Benjamin Zephaniah (Viking, 1994) Copyright © Benjamin Zephaniah, 1994. Reproduced by permission of Penguin Books Ltd

Image of Benjamin Zephaniah on back cover, contents page and page 48 © Susannah Ireland/ REX

Quote on page 49: "Bought and Sold", Benjamin Zephaniah, *Too Black, Too Strong*, (Bloodaxe Books, 2001)

Image on page 51: Triumph TR7 by Charles01 licenced for re-use under the creative commons licence http://creativecommons.org/licenses/by-sa/3.0/deed.en

With thanks to Alamy, CGTextures.com, Clipart.com, iStockphoto.com, Look and Learn, Rex Features and Thinkstockphotos.co.uk for permission to use the stock images in this book.

Leonardo da Vinci

"A mind without parallel"

written by Rebecca Tate

June 1466 Leonardo's heart thudded in his chest as he and his father approached the artist's workshop. At 14, Leonardo was old enough to leave home and start an **apprenticeship**, and he desperately wanted to be an artist. His father was not so sure, convinced that there was more money to be made elsewhere.

"Verrocchio (Ver-oh-key-oh)!" his father shouted as they ducked through the doorway. They were greeted by the pungent smell of paint and the chatter of busy artists.

"Da Vinci (Vin-chee)! Welcome!" came the reply from Verrocchio. "Come to show me your son's work?"

"Yes — he's brought his best drawings. Please tell me whether there is any point in him continuing with this passion of his."

Leonardo stepped forward, clutching a stack of drawings to his chest. He spread them out on the table and held his breath.

Silence. Then, finally, the artist spoke.

Leonardo lived with his mother in a small town in Italy until he was 14. He then moved to the Italian city of Florence to live with his father.

"These are very promising. He will make an exceptional artist if he puts his mind to it. I have a room here for another apprentice to move in — will you let me train him?"

Leonardo's father hesitated and looked at his son. The boy was standing in the centre of the room, slowly turning his head, taking in the wonderful chaos of the workshop. On his face was an enchanted smile.

"How soon can he start?"

Modern-day Florence.

An Artistic Education

JULY 1469 "What *are* you doing?" asked Lorenzo, smirking at Leonardo's painting.

"I'm trying a new type of paint," explained Leonardo eagerly. "**Egg tempera** dries too quickly. These new oil paints allow me to work with the paint for longer and the colours are much more vivid. They don't need mixing with egg yolk either, so we won't need to keep those smelly chickens in the workshop anymore!"

"Well, it looks ridiculous," said Lorenzo, flicking a speck of paint at Leonardo. "Has Master Verrocchio seen this yet? He won't be pleased — you're supposed to be doing what you're told, not playing with paint!"

Verrocchio's main occupation was creating artworks to sell. He produced so much that he needed apprentices to help him. This meant they had to learn a huge range of skills including painting, sculpture, making suits of armour and silverwork.

July 1469

Dear Diary,

Another exhausting day here in the workshop. I was dead on my feet by the time Verrocchio let us head upstairs to bed. The day began with the usual chore of mixing paint. But today things were a bit different. For the first time I got to grind up lapis lazuli (laz-you-lie) stones to make a beautiful blue paint. These stones are incredibly expensive, so being chosen to grind them shows how much Verrocchio trusts me.

I haven't even told you the best part of today yet! I showed Verrocchio the oil paints I've been trying out but he dismissed them, telling me that I have more important things to do. I was offended at first, but then he asked me to help with one of his paintings! It's of a boy and an angel, and I'm to paint a small dog and a fish. It doesn't sound like much, but this is the next step on my journey to becoming an independent artist and having a workshop of my own! Hopefully he will approve of my work and I will be asked to contribute more to his paintings in the future. I will finally be able to prove myself to him.

I have written to Father to tell him about the painting. Hopefully it will make him proud of me. It is late now, and I must go to sleep. I cannot wait for morning!

Coming of Age

MARCH 1473 Sweeping the sheet off the painting with a flourish, Leonardo watched his master's face closely. Leonardo had been allowed to paint one of the angels on Verrocchio's latest painting but he had not followed the original drawing his master had done — would he be angry? Leonardo's palms began to sweat.

A shadow passed over Verrocchio's face as he peered closely at Leonardo's angel. He sighed deeply. "My boy, you have nothing more to learn from me," he said, turning away. "I shall never pick up a paintbrush again — I will never be able to paint like that. I will devote myself to other forms of art. You are ready to begin selling your own paintings, and, in a few years, you will be ready to set up a workshop of your own."

Leonardo looked stricken. He had never intended to upset the man who had taught him so much. Verrocchio took one more look at his best student, and then walked slowly out of the room.

APRIL 1477 Leonardo was trying in vain to organise his dusty, slightly shabby workshop in time for the arrival of his new apprentice. Three weeks ago he had said an emotional goodbye to Verrocchio and moved out of his workshop. Now he was making the terrifying leap into independence.

Leonardo knew he was fortunate to have studied under a great man like Verrocchio. He had learnt many diverse skills from him, but he wanted to teach his own apprentices even more. He was determined to give them a rounded education, not only in art, but also in geometry, mathematics, design and engineering. He would teach them everything he knew.

There was a timid knock at the door.

"Come in, come in!" Leonardo called to the boy hovering in the doorway, "Let's get started!"

This is the painting that proved Leonardo's skills to Verrocchio. Leonardo painted the angel on the left.

New Beginnings

February 1482 Leonardo looked up as he rode through the city gates. He couldn't help but wonder whether he was doing the right thing in leaving Florence. He'd run his own workshop here for five years, but Milan boasted other opportunities. Leonardo still loved to paint, but he wanted to take on new challenges as well. For months, he had been designing innovative contraptions, and his plan was to try to convince the Duke of Milan to hire him to construct some of them.

Placing a hand over his pocket, Leonardo felt the edges of a letter through the cloth. On it rested his dreams of a career as an engineer. With hope in his heart, he guided his horse along the stony road away from Florence. He didn't look back.

February 1482

Dear Sir,

I am writing to offer my services at your court. I am skilled in designing weapons of war, such as armoured ships and cannons that are able to fire multiple cannonballs at once, as well as city defences that can survive attacks. These ideas have never been seen before, and will allow you to repel any enemy foolish enough to attack you.

I am also an artist, better than any other living man. I can produce beautiful paintings for you, and I have already begun to plan a sculpture of a magnificent bronze horse to glorify your family. It will be as tall as four grown men and will be a fitting tribute to your great father.

I am a gifted musician and I will charm your guests with my singing and playing. In addition, I can create unique and beautiful new instruments to play for you.

No man on earth can offer a wider range of skills. My reputation in Florence is second to none, and I am sure you will agree that employing me would benefit you and your city. I look forward to your response.

Yours sincerely,

Leonardo da Vinci

A Sensation at Court

AUGUST 1483 Leonardo had been a familiar face in the Duke's court for six months, but today he had something special up his sleeve — his lyre. It wasn't just any old lyre though — it was made of shining silver and shaped like a horse's head.

"Leonardo! Play for us!" ordered the Duke with a flick of his hand.

Leonardo took a seat by a sour-looking man who was furiously clutching a plain, wooden lyre. Leonardo began to play a mournful tune, the notes tumbling from the instrument like leaves falling from a tree, and his melancholy voice echoing around the room.

Slowly, conversation in the hall began to die down as, one by one, people fell under the spell of Leonardo's voice. Here was something no one had heard before. *This* was music!

Leonardo's lyre was a stringed instrument a bit like a violin. The strings could either be played with a bow or plucked.

16TH MARCH 1485 "I cannot stand by and do nothing!" the Duke complained. "My advisors tell me that this is a bad omen. Disaster will befall the city! Leonardo, you have always counselled me honestly and wisely. Tell me what is happening."

"An eclipse of the Sun is perfectly natural, and nothing to be afraid of," explained Leonardo. "The Moon is moving in front of the Sun and blocking its light. Come and see the simple device I have made so we can watch it safely." He gestured to a wooden frame propped up in front of the window. Inside the frame was a parchment screen with a tiny hole in the middle. Below it was a blank sheet of parchment.

Leonardo extinguished the room's candles and showed the Duke a tiny image of the Sun projected onto the paper through the pinprick. The shadowy Moon concealed over half of the Sun, so only a thin crescent remained. The two men watched, speechless, as the Moon gradually consumed more and more of the Sun.

Eventually, an eerie darkness fell outside and the two men wandered into the courtyard, staring at the ring of light in the sky.

The Duke's castle.

Chasing Dreams

SEPTEMBER 1486 Leonardo wandered along a row of brightly coloured stalls in Milan's busy market. The calls of vegetable sellers rose above the squawking of chickens and the music of street performers. The scent of spices mingled with the stench of animal dung. Here, you could buy anything from paint to pearls, from cotton to coal.

Above the din, Leonardo heard a faint tweeting sound. Looking around, he spotted a cage containing a small white bird. He peered through the bars at the tiny, trapped creature.

"How much for the bird?" he asked a man nearby.

Leonardo loved all animals, and was a vegetarian for most of his life.

"Two **soldi**," the man replied, smiling as Leonardo gave him the coins.

Leonardo crouched down and carefully undid the catch of the cage. He watched in wonder as the tiny bird hopped over to the door, looked straight at Leonardo and then took flight, soaring up into the cloudless sky. Leonardo grabbed his notebook and began to sketch a bird's delicate wing.

JULY 1489 Leonardo was finally ready to present his idea for a flying machine to the Duke. His thoughts had been consumed by the idea for three years. This was the moment of truth — would the Duke give him the money he needed?

"Sire," he began, his voice trembling slightly, "I believe that with your support I can build a flying machine and take to the air like a bird." He handed over his designs.

The Duke let out a guffaw. "Man cannot fly! Do not waste a second more on this fantasy. Instead you shall build me the bronze horse you promised when you arrived in Milan."

"As you wish," Leonardo replied quietly. Yes, the enormous sculpture would be a challenge, but he *would not* give up on his dream of flight.

Leonardo (second from the right) at the cour of the Duke of Milan (second from the left).

Unfulfilled Promises

JULY 1493 Leonardo's thoughts were full of despair. He had been so confident that he could make the bronze statue! Now, after four years of work, Leonardo had only made a full-size clay model of the statue. The Duke was keen to see the finished statue, and was growing impatient with Leonardo's excuses. To add to Leonardo's troubles, a rumour about the horse was being circulated in Florence by a young artist called Michelangelo: that Leonardo was a fool to try to cast such a colossal statue. Leonardo knew that if he failed, he would anger the Duke and destroy his reputation in Florence as well as Milan.

Casting a Bronze Horse Statue

Making a mould

© Dennis Hallinan / Alamy

1. *Choose a pose for your horse. To make it stable, it should have at least three of its feet on the ground.*
2. *Make a full-size model out of clay.*
3. *Coat your clay model with plaster to make a mould. Break off the plaster in large sections.*
4. *Coat the inside of each plaster section with a layer of wax about 10 cm thick.*
5. *Join the plaster sections together, still containing the wax, and fill the hollow wax shape with plaster.*
6. *Hammer pins through the mould to attach it to the new plaster on the inside.*

Casting

1. *Place the mould into a pit in the ground. (Lay the mould on its side so the pit doesn't need to be deep enough to fit the statue upright.)*
2. *Heat the mould until all the wax melts and flows out of the mould, leaving an empty space between the two layers of plaster. Then, pour molten bronze into this space.*
3. *Allow the bronze to cool completely.*

Finishing touches

1. *Remove the mould and hoist up your horse so it is upright.*
2. *Sand down any rough areas, and polish the finished statue.*

Dreams and Dust

DECEMBER 1499 Leonardo grabbed a pile of notebooks and flung them into his trunk on top of an unfinished painting and some leather shoes. He had to leave. Fast.

He cursed the Duke for his foolishness. The King of France had long claimed that Milan belonged to him, but the Duke had ignored the signs of danger. In May, the French army had advanced into Italy, heading directly for Milan. The Duke had fled in panic, leaving the city defenceless. The French had occupied Milan three months ago. At first, the city had remained peaceful, but now conditions were becoming unbearable. Over the past week, rioting had spread through the city like wildfire, and the French soldiers had begun to execute people loyal to the Duke.

After leaving Milan, Leonardo returned to Florence to restart his career there.

Milan had become a second home to Leonardo. He had created his two greatest masterpieces here — his wall painting of the *Last Supper* and his giant clay horse. He desperately wished he could take them with him.

JUNE 1500 Leonardo's pen raced across the pages of his notebook as his hand struggled to keep up with his latest thoughts about geometry. The door flew open and his apprentice, Tommaso, burst in waving a letter.

"Master, I have terrible news!" he blurted, pausing to catch his breath. "Last month French crossbowmen began to use your beautiful clay horse for target practice. They fired arrows at it relentlessly until there was nothing left but dust and rubble."

Leonardo bowed his head, tears in his eyes. "And that is that," he whispered. "My dream of a majestic bronze horse will remain just that — a dream."

Leonardo's 'Last Supper'.

A Great Rivalry

October 1504 A group of apprentices sat out in the square, enjoying the clear autumnal air. As Leonardo hurried past, one called out to him.

"Leonardo! We are discussing literature. Can you explain this passage to us?"

Spotting one of his rivals, Leonardo seized his chance. "Look, there's the great and mighty Michelangelo. He *must* have an opinion about it. He has opinions about *everything*!"

Michelangelo spun around, his nostrils flaring: "Explain it yourself! Although I can't see why they'd want *your* opinion — you couldn't even finish one bronze statue!" Before Leonardo could retort, Michelangelo strutted away, his satchel slung nonchalantly over his shoulder. The apprentices looked at each other awkwardly and turned away from the great artist, who had been reduced to a red-faced child.

Three months later Leonardo was in a splendid hall in Florence, sketching a painting to go on the west wall. He had been hired to paint a large, action-packed battle scene, and his drawing showed rearing horses, ferocious warriors and glinting steel.

Suddenly, Leonardo felt a presence behind him. Whirling round, he saw Michelangelo standing in the doorway. "What are you doing here?" he asked abruptly.

"I'm here to paint the east wall," Michelangelo replied. "It's going to be a battle scene." He glanced at Leonardo's sketch. "You know, if you spent less time drawing your pointless flying toys you could become a much better artist," he sneered.

"I could never be content with having only one skill," Leonardo replied icily, as he stalked out of the room.

He couldn't stand to be in the presence of that hateful man, but he was short of money so he needed the payment for this painting. There was nothing for it — he would just have to ignore his rival's taunts.

A copy of Leonardo's battle scene. The original painting became damaged and was painted over.

A Dream of Flight

March 1505 Leonardo's apprentices, Tommaso and Salai (Sal-eye), held the canvas wings firmly as Leonardo tightened the leather straps of his great bird. He'd waited his whole life for this; today, he would fly! It had taken years to find a patron willing to pay for the materials for his flying machine, but five months ago Roberto Marini, one of the richest merchants in Florence, had agreed to fund it. Now, it was ready for its first test.

From his position at the top of the hill, Leonardo could see the whole of Florence spread out beneath him, surrounded by forbidding stone walls and divided neatly in two by a mighty river. Its miniature houses marched off into the distance, and he could see the dome of the cathedral rising up from the tangle of streets.

Giving a shout, the apprentices heaved the machine forwards, rolling it down a makeshift runway that led to the edge of a cliff. They pushed the wings up into the air as they let go of the bird, cheering and waving. Leonardo jerked the wings into motion by pushing down on the pedals with his feet and they slowly flapped up and down. As he rolled faster, it became harder to flap the cumbersome wings. The edge of the cliff loomed closer. There wasn't enough room! He reached the edge of the precipice and shot out into the void, hoping against hope that his fragile wings would hold him up. They didn't.

As he plunged downwards, memories flashed before Leonardo's eyes. A crib. A toy bird hanging down from the ceiling, drifting in a slow circle above his head. And then a bird fluttering in through the window and landing by his shoulder. The bird brushing its soft feathers against Leonardo's face and then flying off again. Leonardo had always know that he was destined to fly.

With a smash, Leonardo and his beloved flying contraption collided with the ground. Winded, he struggled to his feet, scraps of canvas and leather all around him. His first flight had been a disaster, but he would not give up. New designs already buzzed around his restless mind.

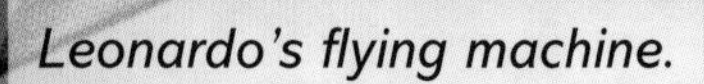

Leonardo's flying machine.

A Lady's Mysterious Smile

JANUARY 1507 Alone in his workshop, Leonardo swirled another drop of white paint onto his palette and turned back to his painting. Closing his eyes, he cast his mind back to the day he had first seen Lisa. At the time, it had been more than two years since he had picked up a paintbrush. He had spent years chasing dreams of flying, but the moment he saw her face, he knew he had to paint her. There was something mysterious about her eyes, and she had a beautiful, half-smiling expression which he was desperate to capture. The only problem was, he just couldn't seem to get it right. It had been four years since he had begun the painting and he must have drawn and redrawn her smile a hundred times!

Today, the 'Mona Lisa' is one of the most famous paintings in the world. It was stolen from a gallery in 1911 and found two years later. It has also been attacked several times.

Another memory floated into his mind — the day he had begun to paint her. He could hear the gentle song of the musician and the puns of the **jesters**, all hired to entertain the lady as he painted.

Suddenly, the delicate window of his memory was shattered by a voice.

"Master, do you need anything?" asked Salai, entering the room.

"Yes, I need some more white paint," replied Leonardo, trying to regain his focus.

"But Master, surely the painting is finished?"

"My boy, I will never *finish* painting this lady. I will only be forced to abandon the attempt. My memory is full of her beauty, but I cannot seem to make my hands do her justice," Leonardo replied sadly. And with those words, he took up his brush once more.

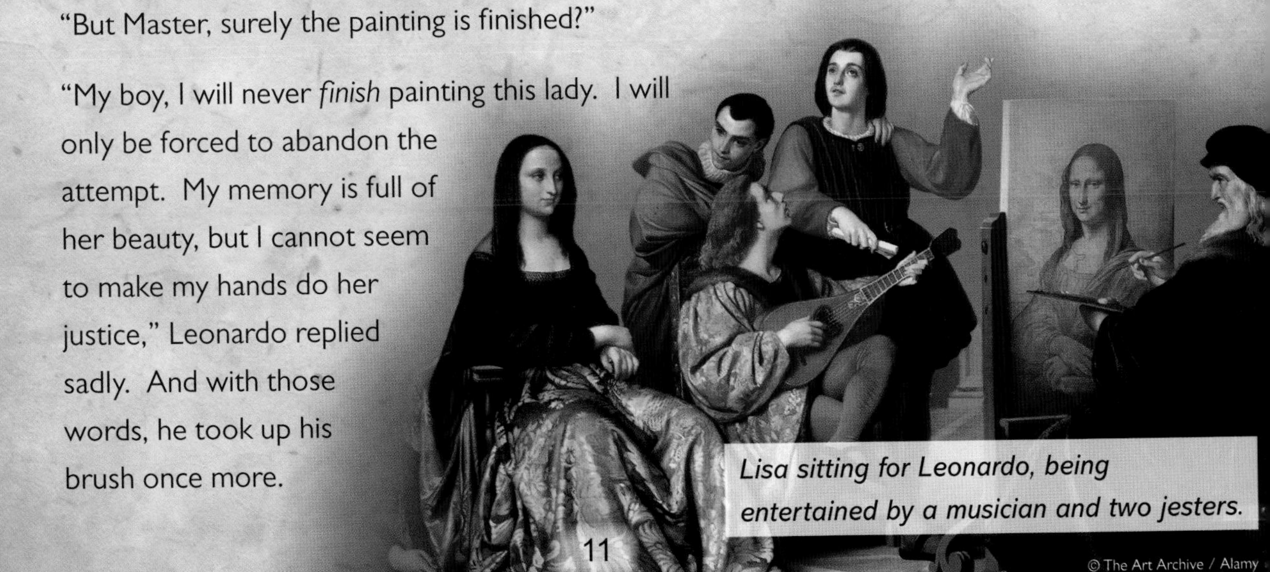

Lisa sitting for Leonardo, being entertained by a musician and two jesters.

A Man of Wisdom

TWO YEARS LATER As Salai watched his master staring at his precious *Mona Lisa* once more, a question rose to the surface of his mind.

"Master, if you love painting so much, why do you do so many other things as well? Why have you not devoted yourself entirely to painting?" he asked.

Leonardo thought for a moment, and then spoke: "When I was a boy, I did not have many friends, so I wandered alone over the hills surrounding Florence. One day I stumbled across a dark cave. I was terrified to think what horrors could be lurking inside. As I peered at the wall of darkness, my ears tried to trick me into thinking I heard the snoring of a great beast. However, as frightened as I was, another force held me in its grip and stopped my feet from running away. Can you think what it was?"

"Curiosity?" guessed Salai.

"Exactly. I *had* to know what hid in the cave, even if it was terrifying. Curiosity drives me. If I think of a question, I *must* know the answer, no matter what the subject is."

"And? What was in the cave?"

"Oh, nothing."

DA VINCI'S NOTEBOOKS

Leonardo da Vinci died in 1519 at the age of 67. As well as sculptures and paintings, he left behind several notebooks full of sketches and notes on many topics.

Anatomy

Da Vinci studied human **anatomy** extensively, sketching muscles and organs. He used these drawings to help him accurately paint the human form, and he criticised other artists, like Michelangelo, who painted men with too many muscles. Unfortunately, he never published his work, so it did not help advance medical science at the time.

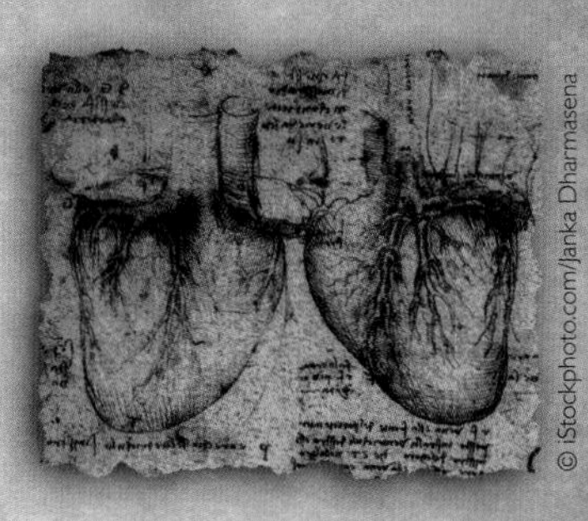

Inventions and architecture

© iStockphoto.com/Janka Dharmasena

Da Vinci has been credited with inventing many modern-day items such as tanks, helicopters (see image) and parachutes. He also made improvements to bridges, windmills and digging machines.

To entertain the King of France, da Vinci once made a clockwork lion, which moved along the ground, then opened up its jaws to reveal a bunch of flowers.

He also designed an 'ideal city', complete with roads, buildings and canals.

Puzzles and codes

Da Vinci loved word puzzles called rebuses, where pictures represent words. He wrote many of these in his notebooks, as well as puns he had made up.

His notebooks are full of mirror writing. Some people think this was a code, but others argue that it was simply because he was left-handed.

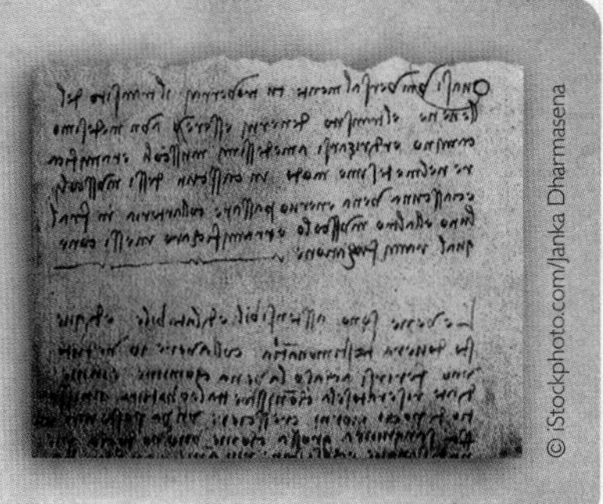

© iStockphoto.com/Janka Dharmasena

Leonardo da Vinci was a fascinating figure, whose talents stretch far beyond the art that he is most famous for. His notebooks give us an intriguing glimpse into the mind of a genius.

Glossary

anatomy — The study of the bodies of humans or animals

apprenticeship — A period of on-the-job training, usually in a practical skill

egg tempera — A type of paint made by mixing coloured powders with egg yolk

jester — Someone who is employed to tell jokes and entertain people

soldi — Currency used in medieval Florence

Wolfgang Amadeus Mozart

"Child genius"

written by Claire Boulter

Wolfgang Amadeus Mozart was born in January 1756 in Salzburg (a city in modern-day Austria). His father was a professional violinist.

MARCH 1759 Wolfgang crouched on the floor next to his sister Nannerl, listening intently as she whispered something to him in the secret language they had invented.

"Nannerl!" their father's voice intruded on their game. "Come along, it's time for your music lesson."

Nannerl leapt to her feet, dropped the paper crown she was holding and dashed from the room without a backward glance. Wolfgang frowned; ever since their father had started teaching Nannerl to play the **harpsichord**, he had felt like she was part of a secret club that he didn't belong to. He glanced at his mother, who was busy with her embroidery and didn't look up. He stood up and crept through the house, following the sweet sounds that rolled and tumbled through the still air.

Wolfgang peeked round the door of the music room, entranced by the sight of his sister's hands skimming gracefully across the keys. As he watched, his fingers began to move restlessly against his leg in time with the music.

Nannerl paused in her playing as their father, Leopold, bent to point out a difficult part of the music. Wolfgang crept closer. When he was within reach of the keyboard, he tentatively stretched out a finger and pressed a key.

"No Wolfie, you're too young to—" Leopold broke off as Wolfgang continued to pick out notes, recreating the sounds he had heard Nannerl making. After a few minutes he paused and looked up at his father.

"Well, young man," said Leopold hoarsely, "perhaps it's time I started teaching you too."

A Royal Encounter

Wolfgang started composing his own music when he was five. His father wrote some of the pieces down and they still exist today.

OCTOBER 1762 Wolfgang stood next to Nannerl, gazing wide-eyed around the vast room of the palace in Vienna. Everywhere he looked he saw something wonderful — the chandeliers dripping with sparkling crystals; the grand portraits of solemn men and women gazing from heavy gold frames; the lofty ceiling, upon which gods reclined amid feathery clouds. Most of all, he couldn't take his eyes off the harpsichord — he had never seen a more beautiful instrument. His fingers itched to touch the polished ivory keys.

A respectful hush fell over the room as a tall, stately woman entered. Wolfgang realised that this must be Empress Maria Theresa, the rich, powerful lady they had come to play for. He bowed deeply, as he had been taught, aware of Nannerl curtseying at his side.

As the Empress settled herself on a chair, Wolfgang and Nannerl crossed over to the harpsichord. Wolfgang's hands trembled slightly as he sat down, feeling the eyes of the room upon him, but his nerves were forgotten as soon as he began to play. He and Nannerl were perfectly in time, their fingers flying across the keyboard. The music surged through Wolfgang's veins, sweet and intoxicating. If only this feeling could last forever.

THREE MONTHS LATER Wolfgang leaned from the carriage to give the Empress a final hug, taking care not to crease the fine, gold-trimmed suit that she had given him as a present. He marvelled that he had ever felt scared of her — she and the rest of the royal court had treated the Mozarts like family, and she doted on Wolfgang.

As the carriage pulled away, bearing them back towards Salzburg, Wolfgang sighed. He'd grown used to the royal life; he would miss the treats, the fun and the attention.

Nannerl and Wolfgang playing for the Empress Maria Theresa.

Another String to the Bow

FEBRUARY 1763 The Mozarts' music room was full of chat and laughter as the musicians gathered. Wolfgang stood apart, remembering Vienna: the audience listening in spellbound silence, the thunderous applause, the admiring looks. Why shouldn't he have that here too?

He had been experimenting with the violin, and he knew he could play the piece they were discussing. Tugging at his father's sleeve, he stated, "I shall play **second violin** today, Papa."

His father laughed and ruffled his hair. "Ah, Wolfie, at least wait until you've started your lessons! When you're older you shall play with us, but not yet. Sit quietly and listen."

Wolfgang's cheeks turned red. He felt his eyes fill with tears, and he turned angrily away.

"Why not let the boy try it, Leopold?" One of the other musicians spoke quickly.

Leopold sighed and waved a hand in acceptance. His tears forgotten, Wolfgang grabbed a violin and, finding his place in the music, joined in with the other musicians. One by one they stopped playing, until only Wolfgang's violin could be heard, its notes true and sweet.

How to play the violin

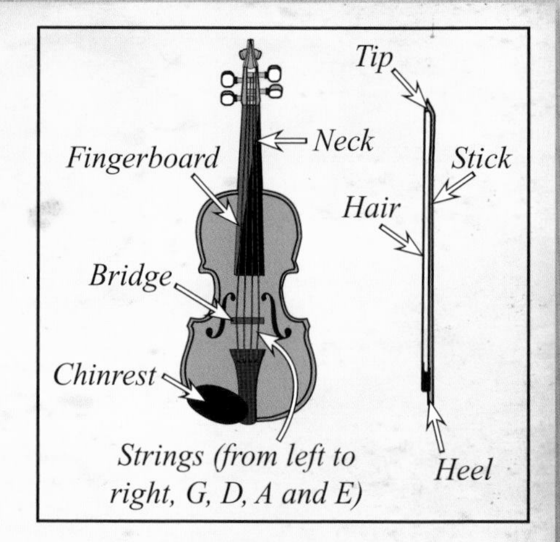

Holding the violin:

1. Place the violin on your left shoulder and rest your chin on the chinrest.
2. Hold the neck of the violin loosely in your left hand, keeping your wrist straight. The neck should rest between your thumb and first finger.
3. Curl the fingers of your left hand so their tips are just above the violin strings.

Holding the bow:

1. Pick up the bow with your right hand, holding it by the stick close to the heel.
2. Rest the hair of the bow horizontally on the A string, about half way between the bridge and the end of the fingerboard.

Playing notes:

1. Pull the bow across the string. This will produce a note — an A.
2. Play a different note by moving the bow across a different string, or by pressing the string you are playing against the fingerboard.

On the Road

APRIL 1764 Wolfgang pulled out his handkerchief, wiped a small clean circle on the grimy window and peered down into the narrow London street below. The room he was in was dark and cramped; the stench of stagnant water and boiled cabbage lingered in the air; muffled shouts drifted up from the street. But there was a real bed in the corner, the room wasn't moving and he had it all to himself — right now, that was good enough.

He, Nannerl and their parents had been travelling for nearly a year. They had toured Europe, playing for kings and queens, princes and princesses. The performances had been superb, but the endless travelling had been awful. The roads were rough, the horse-drawn carriage small and jolting, so its occupants were bumped around for hour after painful hour. Even worse had been the crossing from Calais to Dover — the small boat had been tossed like a matchstick on the stormy sea. Wolfgang groaned as he remembered the queasy feeling in his stomach, the rough planks beneath his hands as he leaned over the side to... no, better not to think of that, he'd make himself ill again.

*In the 18th century, people were fascinated by **child prodigies**. Wolfgang and Nannerl were invited to play in many royal courts.*

Wolfgang determinedly turned his mind to happier matters. Tomorrow they would perform for King George III of England!

OCTOBER 1765 In a darkened room in the Hague, Nannerl lay as still and pale as death. Wolfgang knelt beside her, clutching her icy hand to his cheek, as the priest murmured the **last rites**. A huge weight seemed to press down on his chest, and he struggled to breathe. How could he cope without his beloved sister?

Suddenly, Leopold burst into the room, accompanied by a man Wolfgang recognised as the royal doctor. The doctor strode over to the bed, gently touched Nannerl's waxy skin and peered into her foggy eyes. Muttering to himself, he grabbed a small bottle from his bag, uncorked it and trickled a few drops into her mouth. Wolfgang bit his lip as, slowly, Nannerl's cheeks began to regain a little colour and her hand stirred in his.

Nannerl made a full recovery from her illness.

A Wandering Minstrel

March 1770 Wolfgang strolled down the street, enjoying the gentle caress of the spring sun on his face. He seated himself on the stone steps of a huge building, as ornate and gleaming as a wedding cake. He leaned back against a sun-warmed marble column and closed his eyes. From an open window he could hear a young woman singing softly, and in the distance a church bell joyfully pealed out a melody. Italy was a fine place, he reflected.

He had been touring for three months now, playing in theatres, concert halls and royal courts. He had learnt so much, and he felt confident that a glittering career stretched before him. The only cloud on the horizon was Nannerl, or rather, the lack of her. She hadn't been allowed to come on this tour. Wolfgang missed her laughter, her company, her advice on his music... It just wasn't the same without her.

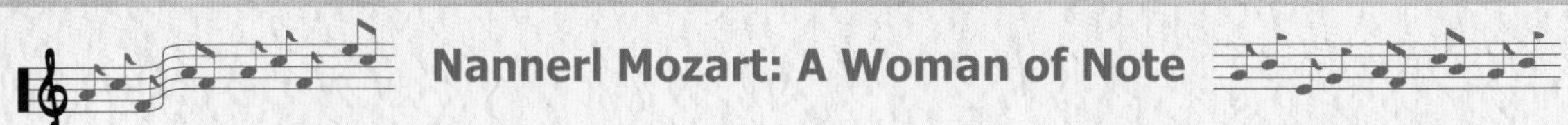

Nannerl Mozart: A Woman of Note

As a child, Maria Anna Mozart (known as Nannerl) was described as a 'genius', she toured with Wolfgang and was thought to be just as talented. Now, none of her music remains and few people have even heard of her. So why is her story so different from his?

The underlying reason is that Nannerl was a woman. When she was a child, it was acceptable for her to perform as a 'child prodigy', but it was considered immodest for grown women to perform in public. When she grew up, Nannerl therefore had to give up her public performances.

In the 18th century, a woman's role was to marry and have children, rather than work for a living. Once girls of Nannerl's social class reached eighteen, they were expected to marry wealthy men. Such men would have been embarrassed to have a wife who performed in public, so Nannerl could no longer perform in case it put off potential husbands.

Because Nannerl could not have a career in music, her parents did not support her musical talent as they did with Wolfgang. Leopold Mozart thought it was important for Wolfgang to tour Italy, learning about Italian music and meeting new contacts to help him find work. Such a trip would have been wasted on Nannerl, who could not apply such knowledge or use such contacts. As a result, she was left at home in Salzburg.

Nannerl's chance of success as a musician was minimal from the moment she was born. Had she been male, her name may now be as famous as that of her brother.

Easter 1770 Wolfgang leaned back in the hard, wooden pew as the priest spoke, drinking in the vivid, incredibly lifelike paintings on the wall and ceiling of the Sistine (Sis-teen) Chapel. As dusk cloaked the corners of the chapel in shadow, he could almost believe that the figures were about to spring to life: that Eve would bite into the ripe, sweet fig clutched in her hand, that Adam would step out of Eden and walk the Earth, that God Himself would turn his fearsome gaze upon the mere mortals below. Wolfgang shivered.

At that moment, an unearthly music filled the air. Wolfgang sat transfixed as the beautiful sound swelled and rippled around him. This must be the *Miserere* (Miz-uh-rare-ee), the famous composition played only at Easter — it was so jealously guarded that writing it down or performing it anywhere but the Sistine Chapel was forbidden. As the last note faded into silence, Wolfgang leapt to his feet and, unaware of the annoyed looks of the people around him, dashed from the chapel and sprinted back to his lodgings.

Shouldering open the door, he snatched up a piece of paper, and began scribbling furiously. Hearing a noise, he spun round in sudden fear, but there was nobody there. An hour later, he sat back, exhausted. He looked over what he had written. Yes! That was it, he was certain — the full score of the fifteen-minute song he had heard, note for precious note.

Three months later Wolfgang clasped his hands together to stop them shaking. He had made a copy of Miserere just for himself, so he would always remember it, but somehow the copy he had made had become public. Now the Pope had summoned him here — who knew what terrible punishment lay in store for him?

The Pope swept into the room and regarded Wolfgang sternly. "As you know, the *Miserere* has been a closely guarded secret for over a century. Writing it down is punishable by **excommunication**." Wolfgang whimpered, but the Pope merely held up a hand. "However," he paused, "in this case, I think we can make an exception. Your remarkable talent is a gift from God, so your crime will be pardoned. All over Europe people are marvelling at the piece so, in recognition of the glory you have brought to the Catholic Church, I am going to award you the **Order of the Golden Spur**."

Tears flowed down Wolfgang's cheeks as, stammering his heartfelt thanks, he stooped to kiss the Pope's hand.

Pope Clement XIV.

Taking a Gamble

Wolfgang moved back to Salzburg in 1773 and took a job as a musician in the court of the Prince-Archbishop, Count Colloredo (Col-o-ray-doe).

AUGUST 1777 Wolfgang threw down his quill and rubbed his eyes. He was pleased with his new composition, but he knew it wouldn't get anything like the credit that it deserved.

After four years, he was sick of this job. His salary was low; there was no opportunity to travel because he was at Count Colloredo's beck and call; and there was nowhere to perform the operas that he yearned to write. He was sick of Salzburg too — a quiet little backwater where nobody seemed to care about music.

Gazing out of his window over the muddy grey water of the river, he made up his mind. It was time to leave, time to live, time to seek his fortune elsewhere.

"Salzburg is no place for my talents... there is no theatre, no opera; and even if they wanted one, who is there to sing?"

DECEMBER 1778 Wolfgang pulled his threadbare coat more tightly around himself, clutched his violin to his chest and walked on down the icy street in the centre of Munich (Mew-nick), head bowed against the pitiless wind and spiteful, stinging sleet. It was a long walk back to his lodgings, but he couldn't afford a cab.

His quest to find work elsewhere hadn't gone well. True, he had been well-received everywhere he went: Mannheim (Man-hime), Paris, Strasbourg, Munich... Everyone wanted to hear him play, but nobody wanted to give him a job. He had **pawned** everything of value that he owned; all he had left was his violin. His choice was stark — pawn his violin, or return to Salzburg and hope that Count Colloredo would give him a job.

Wolfgang sighed. There wasn't really any choice — he could never part with his beloved violin.

An Undignified Exit

In 1779, Wolfgang was employed by the Count as an organist and to help run the court orchestra. In the 18th century, musicians were seen as servants and weren't treated with much respect, which Wolfgang resented.

March 1781 Wolfgang stood with the other musicians, listening to the excited hum of conversation. They had been called here to Vienna by Count Colloredo to play at the **accession** of the new Emperor, for which they would each receive a princely wage. As the other musicians drifted off, Wolfgang was held back by a sharp command.

"You, Mozart, stay behind!"

Wolfgang forced a polite smile and turned to face the Count.

The Count glanced up from the book he was writing in. "You won't be playing at the accession," he said curtly. Wolfgang started to stammer a protest, but the Count shoved his chair back and stood, his eyes blazing. "Don't argue with me, boy. My decision is final. Now get out of my sight."

Wolfgang stormed from the room, his hands so tightly clenched that he would later find four bloody half-moons etched on each palm.

Three months later Wolfgang took a deep breath and pushed open the door to the Count's lobby, his letter of resignation clutched firmly in his hand. He had tried to leave twice in the past few months, but he hadn't been allowed. Today, he was determined.

Colloredo's steward, Count Arco, frowned as Wolfgang entered. "You can't make me stay. I must be allowed to leave," Wolfgang said fiercely.

Angered by his tone of voice, Count Arco stood up. "You want to go? Then go! You think we can't do without you, you clown, you rogue?"

Count Arco strode across the room, grabbed Wolfgang by his collar and lifted him bodily towards the door. Dropping him on the floor, he gave him a swift kick in the backside, then slammed the door.

Wolfgang glared at the closed door, then suddenly started to laugh. He might be angry, he might be sore, but at least he was free.

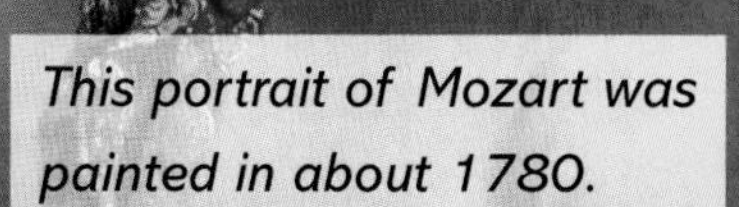

This portrait of Mozart was painted in about 1780.

If Music be the Food of Love

Wolfgang earned money by teaching music to the children of rich families. In the summer, such families travelled to the country to escape the city's heat, so money was tight for Wolfgang.

JULY 1781 A warm breeze drifted through Vienna; outside, people basked in the sun and lolled on the banks of the river. Alone in his room, Wolfgang scribbled frenziedly. A stack of paper covered in musical notes grew on the desk to his right as the pile of blank paper to his left shrank. From time to time he stopped, swung his chair round to the harpsichord and played a few notes. Operas, quartets, serenades... music of all types seemed to bubble up in his mind like water from a spring, and flow freely from his hand.

A soft knock came at the door, and the melody playing in his head stopped abruptly. He cursed under his breath, but his frown disappeared as the door opened to reveal Constanze, one of the daughters of the family he was staying with.

"Dinner is prepared, Wolfgang," she said with a smile, "but we'll wait until you're ready."

Wolfgang gazed after her as she left the room, his lips slightly parted. Here was another reason he must work so hard: he was determined to marry Constanze, but he couldn't hope to win her and her family around unless he could support her.

4TH AUGUST 1782 Wolfgang and Constanze emerged from the gloomy cathedral into bright sunshine. Their wedding had been a quiet affair, with only a handful of people there to witness the event. Beneath his joy, Wolfgang felt a heavy sorrow — he wished his family were here to celebrate, but his mother had died more than a decade ago, and his father didn't approve of his marriage. Nannerl couldn't act without her father's consent, so she too was absent.

Wolfgang shook off his dark thoughts and smiled at his new bride. He was young, he was in love and his career was starting to take off. Who knew what the next stage of his life would hold?

Wolfgang and Constanze on their honeymoon.

JANUARY 1787 As the last note of the final song fell away, Wolfgang wiped the sweat from his brow and took a deep breath. His new opera hadn't been as well received as he had hoped in Vienna, but surely the people of Prague would be more appreciative? He turned to face the audience. Their faces revealed nothing. Mozart could hear his heart hammering in his chest as the silence pressed down on him.

Suddenly, as if a spell had been broken, the audience rose to their feet as one, clapping and cheering, calling for more.

Wolfgang composed the music for an opera, 'The Marriage of Figaro'. It was first performed in Vienna in May 1786. He conducted some of its performances himself.

Prague, 22nd January 1787

My goodness, what an evening! It's late, but I'm far too excited to sleep! I just got back from a girls' trip to the theatre with Mama — we saw a performance of Mozart's new opera, 'The Marriage of Figaro', conducted by the composer himself!

As we entered the theatre, I was almost overwhelmed by the crush of people, the thunder of voices, the scent of expensive perfume. I don't think I have ever seen so many people in one place! I grabbed Mama's hand, and we jostled our way to our seats.

Almost as soon as we had made ourselves comfortable, a deathly hush fell upon the room. Looking round in alarm to see what had caused such a silence, I realised that Mozart had made his way onto the stage — I was surprised to learn that he is a small, slight man, not at all the towering, brooding figure I imagined.

After a moment, the orchestra began to play, and for the next few hours I was transported to another world, swept along in the story of brave Figaro and his true love Susanna, plotting to trick the cruel Count so they can marry without his meddling.

When the opera ended, it took me a moment to return to myself. As I blinked back tears at the happy conclusion, I chanced to look at Mozart — I have never seen a look of such anxiety on anyone's face! I realised that I, and the rest of the audience, had remained silent long after we should have started applauding.

At once, I rose to my feet and started to clap, just as everyone else in the audience did likewise. The noise was like a tidal wave, crashing into every corner of the room. As I looked at Mozart again, I saw that his face was bathed in tears. I felt my heart go out to this man of genius, reduced to tears by a crowd's reaction.

Desperate Times

DECEMBER 1788 Sitting at his desk, Wolfgang picked up the next letter in the pile, skimmed its contents and dropped it on the floor. Another refusal!

He leaned back and picked at a worn patch on the sleeve of his silk jacket. How on earth was he supposed to pay to get it mended? Buoyed up by the success of *The Marriage of Figaro* and his next opera, *Don Giovanni* (Jee-oh-varn-ee), he and Constanze had lived the high life for the past few years — they had rented a grand apartment, hired servants, bought fine clothes... Now though, the commissions for work had stopped coming in, and with them the money.

In 1789, the Austrian Empire was at war with the Turkish Empire. The war was expensive, so people in Vienna had little money spare to spend on music.

He sighed and opened another letter. He recognised the handwriting — it was from his good friend, Michael von Puchberg. His hand started to shake as he read the letter — Michael had agreed to lend him money. Wolfgang could pay off his most pressing debts, and have a little left over for Christmas gifts.

MAY 1789 Wolfgang swallowed nervously as the King of Prussia pored over his new composition. He had thought that he was settled in Vienna, but he couldn't earn enough there to support himself, Constanze and their son, Karl. They couldn't live off loans from friends forever, so here he was again: touring Europe, searching for work.

Wolfgang's operas were still being performed in many countries, but he didn't get any money for them.

"Well," the King spoke at last, "these are certainly excellent. But, well, you know how things are. Money... The wife... I can't offer you any work. I'm truly sorry."

Wolfgang smiled and bowed, but his stomach was as heavy as lead. This had been his last, best chance for work. He would have to return to Vienna empty-handed.

King Frederick William II of Prussia was known for his love of music.

The Swan Song

December 1791 Constanze knelt by the side of Wolfgang's bed, pressing a cold cloth to his aching head. He groaned and struggled to sit up but couldn't find the strength. A treacherous tear crept from his eye as, gently, Constanze lifted the quill from his swollen hand.

Wolfgang died on the 5th December 1791. This statue was erected in Vienna in 1898.

"Just rest a little, my darling," she said softly. "When you wake you can finish your new **Requiem**."

Wolfgang lay back, closed his eyes and let the sound of the masterpiece that he would never finish flood his mind.

UNMASKING MOZART

Since Mozart's death, lots has been written about him — some of it true, some not. Here are a few of the common myths about him, and the truth behind the rumours.

Myth 1: Mozart Died Penniless

This image of Mozart's coffin being carried to the graveyard dates from about 1860.

Many people believe that Mozart died in poverty and was buried in a **pauper's grave**. It is true that he had a cheap funeral, but this was normal for the time — seven years earlier, Emperor Joseph II had announced that funerals were too grand and expensive, and should be simpler. In reality, Mozart's final year was extremely productive and his finances improved. Although he was never rich, he, Constanze and their children always lived comfortably.

Myth 2: Mozart was Murdered by a Rival

Mozart died when he was just 35. People suspected that he had been poisoned, a rumour he had started himself by telling Constanze in 1789, "I am only too conscious... my end will not be long in coming; for sure, someone has poisoned me!" Suspicion fell on Antonio Salieri (Sal-ee-airy), another composer who lived in Vienna. Despite the rumours, there's no evidence that Mozart was poisoned, and still less that Salieri was responsible. On the contrary, Salieri had a better job than Mozart and earned more money, and the two men were on good terms.

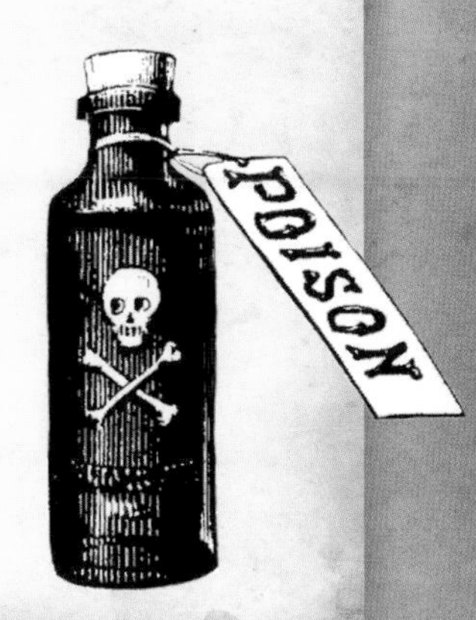

Myth 3: Listening to Mozart Makes You Clever

Since the late 20th century, many people have believed in the 'Mozart effect' — that listening to Mozart's music increases intelligence. As a result, many parents have played Mozart's music to their children and babies, hoping to boost their grades. In 1993, researchers in California found that students performed some tasks slightly better after listening to 10 minutes of Mozart. However, they found that listening to Mozart only increased performance on one task out of a range, and the effect wore off after 15 minutes. Furthermore, later studies found that listening to other types of music produced a similar effect, and in fact children who were played the pop song *Country House* by Blur performed better than children who listened to Mozart.

Mozart's life, death and works have been a source of fascination for scholars, composers and the public. Dozens of myths and legends have sprung up around the great man; we now know some of them to be false, but we may never learn the truth about others.

Glossary

accession — Coming to power

child prodigies — Children who show extraordinary talent in a particular field

excommunication — Banishment from a religion

harpsichord — A musical instrument which was an early version of the piano

last rites — Prayers and blessings said for a Catholic person soon before they die

Order of the Golden Spur — An award given to people who have done a great service to the Catholic church

pauper's grave — A grave paid for by the public, because the dead person's family are too poor. In the past, paupers were sometimes buried in mass graves

pawned — Lent to a dealer in exchange for money. The previous owner of the object can buy it back later; if they don't buy it back in an agreed period, the dealer can sell it on

Requiem — A piece of music written for someone's death, often played at their funeral

second violin — A musical part played by one or more violinists. Often, the first violin plays the main tune and the second violin plays the supporting tune

Charles Dickens

"An author of great character"

written by Holly Poynton

23RD APRIL 1824 Twelve-year-old Charles scurried behind the jailer, taking big gulps of damp air to still his hammering heart and quell his swirling stomach.

Charles's father was thrown into Marshalsea ***debtors' prison****. His wife and youngest children lived with him in his cell. Charles and his elder sister Frances were left to fend for themselves.*

The guard stopped abruptly and inserted a particularly long and rusty key into the skull-shaped lock.

"You've got five minutes," he barked, shoving Charles into the cell.

There, sitting on a thin layer of straw, were his mother, his father and his three younger siblings. Charles sank to his knees and fell into his family's outstretched arms. All anyone could do was weep and murmur. His mother told him he looked thin and worried that he wasn't eating enough. His father asked if there was any news from relatives or friends. His siblings, not really old enough to understand what was happening, were content to hug him and pester him for sweets.

The guard rapped on the bars of the prison door — the signal that Charles's time was almost up. Seized by urgency, Charles's father grasped his son by the shoulders and hissed into his ear.

"Charles, our fates are in your hands now. Write letters, sell possessions, do whatever you can. Raise the money so that we can pay our debts and get out of this infernal place."

Charles only had time to nod as a pair of hands grabbed him roughly by the arm and dragged him back into the dingy passageway.

Charles was allowed to visit his family in prison.

Hard Times

29TH APRIL 1824 Whoops of laughter rang in Charles's ears as he trotted along the pavement. He knew he must look comical — a small boy struggling under the weight of an armchair twice his size — but he was used to ignoring the taunts of passers-by. He ducked down an alley and heaved himself into a gloomy-looking shop.

The Dickens family's experiences with poverty affected Charles deeply. Debtors' prisons appear in several of his novels including 'The Pickwick Papers', 'David Copperfield' and 'Little Dorrit'.

"Master Dickens! Back so soon?" said a raspy voice from the depths of the shop. Two beady eyes watched Charles as he dodged round a pillar of books and almost fell into a haphazard honeycomb of empty pots and pans.

"How much will you give me for the chair?" asked Charles, trying to hide his desperation.

Gnarled fingers plucked at the tattered upholstery. "Six shillings. No more."

Charles reluctantly pocketed the money, and headed back into the street. He'd barely raised a handful of coins — a far cry from the £40 he needed to pay off his father's debts. There had to be another way to raise the money his family desperately needed.

Charles at work in the blacking factory

4TH MAY 1824 "THWACK!" Charles jumped as Mr Biggins's cane landed sharply across his table, and the factory owner's bulbous nose came level with his own.

"I ain't payin' ya to gawp out ov the winda, Dickens! Back ta work!" Charles hastily stuck his brush into the jar of paste and swirled it round — once, twice — before deftly swiping the brush along the edge of a pot.

He'd been working at the blacking factory for several weeks now. He toiled for ten hours a day, six days a week, sticking labels on pots of shoe polish. But as much as he hated it, he knew that he was a lot better off than many children his age.

Stroud, Gloucestershire, 18th August 1827

Dear Sir,

I write to you not only because you are my local MP, but because you are a compassionate, God-fearing man who will not stand by as others suffer.

I know that you take pride in protecting the children of this wonderful country — I remember well your support for the Factory Act of 1819. Thanks to this law, working hours for children were reduced to twelve hours a day, and factories are no longer permitted to employ children under the age of nine. However, this is simply not enough.

Firstly, we must make our mills and factories safer. Have you visited a cotton factory, sir? Then you will know of the terrible din — the machines are so loud they make children deaf before they reach their thirteenth birthday. Then you will know of the poor ventilation — the air is so dusty that workers as young as ten develop breathing problems. Then you will know of the danger — the machines are so ferocious they will easily snap a child's arm. Would you send your own children to this place, sir? Hundreds of children don't have this choice; they must endure these conditions or risk starvation. If they must work in these factories, shouldn't we make them safer?

Secondly, we must end the cruelty these children face at the hands of the managers and foremen. If a child is even a minute late, he will be beaten so severely that he will be bruised for weeks. If a child makes a mistake, the manager will thrash him so hard he may well break a bone. No child is exempt from this treatment and every child lives in fear. Do you treat your children this way, sir? For hundreds of children, this is their way of life; they must tolerate this cruelty or risk homelessness. If they must work in these factories, shouldn't we make them less distressing?

Thirdly, we must reduce working hours. Children toil from 7 am to 7 pm, six days a week. It is common for children to work through their mealtimes if their managers are displeased with their work. Do you work this hard, sir? For hundreds of children, these backbreaking hours are a reality; they must endure exhaustion or risk being sent to the ***workhouse***. *If they must work in these factories, shouldn't we make their hours shorter?*

Sir, thank you for hearing this plea. Take this letter to Parliament and be the voice of those children who cannot defend themselves. Let the men of the Government hear their plight. You have the power to make a difference and to end the strain, suffering and sadness these children face every single day.

Yours faithfully, George Steadman

A New Door Opens

Charles's family were released from prison in 1824 after John Dickens was able to pay off his debts using money he had inherited.

JUNE 1828 Sixteen-year-old Charles whistled as he strolled home. He'd been working as a junior **clerk** in a law firm for over a year now, and he was grateful that his days of gruelling work were behind him.

A newspaper seller stood on the street corner just ahead of him, and was thrusting that evening's edition under the nose of every **well-heeled** gentleman.

"Evenin', sir!" said the seller, waving the newspaper at Charles. "Only tuppence!" Charles dug about in his pockets for a coin to pay the lad and unfolded the paper.

He ignored all the articles about Parliament and even flicked past an entertaining story about a sailor who had got lost on the Thames, before turning to the pages he was after: the latest instalment of a **serialised novel** he had become hooked on.

OCTOBER 1833 Charles took a few determined paces towards *Monthly Magazine*'s front door. Yes, he was definitely going to post the envelope. But then fear and doubt washed over him. What if they read his short story and hated it? What if he became the laughing stock of London? No, best not go through with it and save himself the bother.

He was about to head home when he looked down at the brown envelope in his hand, slightly crinkled by his damp palm. He'd worked on *A Dinner at Poplar Walk* for weeks; it'd be a shame to waste all that effort. He took a few more steps towards the brass letter box, which glinted invitingly in the lamplight. Then, before he even realised what he was doing, he thrust the envelope through the letter box, and heard his manuscript land with a dull thud on the other side of the door.

Charles's first short story, 'A Dinner at Poplar Walk' was first published in December 1833.

A Roaring Success

OCTOBER 1837 Charles heard a knock at his study door followed by a quavering voice.

"Mr Dickens, sir. Sorry to interrupt, but there's a man here to see you." Charles didn't even look up from his writing desk. The maid cleared her throat. "Mr Dickens, sir. Sorr-"

"I heard you the first time, Georgina. Send him away. I am working." Charles reached the end of his sheet of paper and dunked the end of his pen in a small bottle of ink.

"He's very insistent, sir. Says it's important." Before Charles could respond, the man in question barrelled into Charles's study, throwing his hat into the air.

Charles wrote under the pen name 'Boz' and his friend and illustrator, Hablot Knight Browne, used the pen name 'Phiz'. Phiz went on to illustrate most of Dickens's novels.

"Boz! Dearest, dearest Boz!" the man exclaimed, clapping Charles on the back and leaping about. "They've printed forty thousand copies of the final instalment, old boy! Forty thousand!" Charles tossed down his pen.

"Truly, Phiz? Forty thousand copies?" Phiz simply nodded and did a funny little jig on the hearth rug. At once, Charles stood, a beaming smile stretched across his face. "By Jove, forty thousand copies!"

"*The Pickwick Papers* is a phenomenon! It's been more successful than the publishers ever dared imagine! The public and the magazine editors are hungry for more!"

"Well if they want more, then more they shall get! I've been working on a new serial..."

Phiz raised an eyebrow. "Do tell, old chum."

"Well, it's a story about an orphan boy who falls in with a gang of London pickpockets. I think I'm going to call it *Oliver Twist*!"

One of Phiz's illustrations, which appeared in 'The Pickwick Papers'.

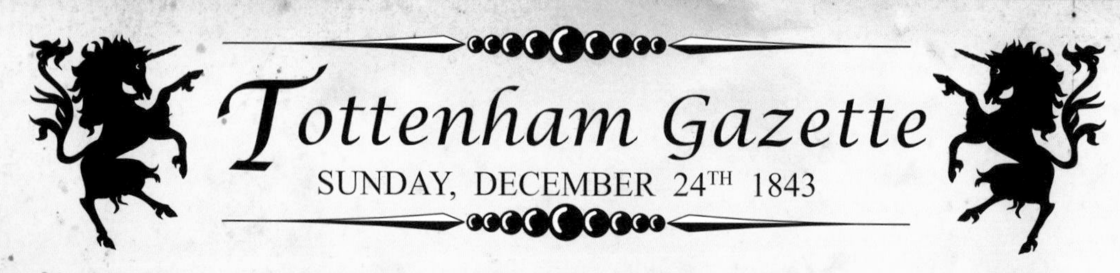

A CHRISTMAS MIRACLE!

Mr Dickens's latest story, *A Christmas Carol,* was published earlier in the week, and sources suggest that it has already sold out, leaving thousands of devotees disappointed. However, for one couple, this was the start of a tale worthy of Mr Dickens himself!

Mr Charles Dickens

John Doncaster, 32, a local teacher, told *The Gazette,* "My wife and I are great admirers of Mr Dickens — we try to save a little money every month so that we can afford to buy his latest instalment. When we heard that he was bringing out a Christmas story we were beside ourselves with excitement — we dipped into our savings pot to cobble together the money we needed to buy a copy.

Disappointment and Distress

"After we finished work, we headed to the bookshop to purchase the book, but the bookseller told us he'd already sold out, and not a single copy was to be had in the whole of London! Well, my wife and I were devastated. We headed homewards, and it soon started to snow. All at once, we were stuck in a blizzard and we had to find shelter to save us from freezing to death.

Shelter and Surprise

"We passed a church and the candles were lit, so we decided to duck inside. When we entered the church, we couldn't believe our eyes — there must've been hundreds of folks crammed inside, most of them poor as can be. I asked a fellow next to me what was happening, and he replied that the vicar of the church was about to start reading a book to the congregation. I asked which book, and I was astounded when he said *A Christmas Carol*!

Christmas Spirit!

"It turns out that the vicar organises regular readings so that his illiterate flock have the chance to enjoy popular stories like everyone else. The vicar had managed to buy one of the last few remaining copies of *A Christmas Carol*, and wanted to share it with his parish. So my wife and I settled into a pew and listened to the wonderful tale. We couldn't believe our luck — it was like something out of a Dickens novel!"

A Man of the People

There was a lot of poverty in 19th century London, and the very poorest people lived in slums — areas of the city which suffered from overcrowding, poor sanitation, crime and disease.

AUGUST 1845 The sun had long since set, but the street Charles wandered down was still a hive of activity. A group of young men in tatty jackets stood loitering in the mouth of an alleyway. They stared at Charles's silk waistcoat with a mixture of distrust and greed. Several stray dogs fought over a chicken bone, their barks echoing down the narrow streets. A skeletal old woman sat at a window coughing and wheezing in the late summer heat, and a barefoot girl of about six or seven sat in the gutter, deaf to the cries of the bawling infant in her lap. She couldn't have been much older than Charles's daughters, Mary and Catherine, and this thought haunted him as he passed her by.

He followed the river of sewage which ran alongside the road. The stench was almost unbearable. He could have easily covered his nose with a fragrant silk handkerchief, but Charles didn't want to protect himself, for this was what he had come to see — some of London's most notorious slums laid bare.

His thoughts turned to his own home, a handsome brick house with beautiful bay windows which overlooked a spacious garden where his wife and children would play happily for hours. He knew that if his father hadn't been released from jail, he too could have lived alongside these people in the slum. He wouldn't have become Charles Dickens, the famous author. He'd be a nothing, a nobody.

Charles knew he had to do more than just write about this poverty — he had to do something, anything, to save as many of these poor souls as he could.

A Friend in Need

OCTOBER 1847 "You're potty, Charles! Urania (You-rain-ee-a) Cottage, indeed." The man shook his head and took another puff of his pipe. "You're going to waste all that money on **ne'er-do-wells**?! If you want to help deserving causes, how about you give *me* the £500!" The man slapped his stout belly and laughed uproariously at his own joke.

Charles sighed; he was getting used to this reaction. "I've already signed the deeds on the property, we've hired a matron and the flyers are being distributed around town next week. We're hoping to interview eligible ladies soon after."

Charles thought back to his tour of the London slums — he knew a **refuge** like Urania Cottage could make a real difference to the lives of poor women in London.

TWO WEEKS LATER "Me name's Sarah Wood, Mr Dickens, sir," said the young girl, pulling a grubby shawl about her shoulders.

"Very good, Miss Wood," said Charles, making a note on the paper in front of him. "And why do you want a place at Urania Cottage?"

"Well, sir, when me Ma died of the **consumption** we was all on our own. Pa had left us when we was just babies, so it were just me and me brother, Tommy. We di'n't 'ave much and we was strugglin', sir. I ain't proud of it, but I started stealin' from folks so I could put food in our bellies." She shifted uncomfortably and looked down at her hands. "Well, I got caught stealin', and I was thrown in prison for a spell. When I came out, Tommy had left and I had no one an' nuthin'. I need a fresh start, sir. I wanna do better for mesel'." Charles lent over the table and stretched out his hand.

"We'd be delighted to have you at Urania Cottage, Miss Wood."

Charles Dickens was critical of how the poor were treated.

By the Book

November 1847 Sarah was led to the front door of Urania Cottage by the matron, and guided into a warm little parlour. She blinked rapidly, afraid the comfortable surroundings would evaporate before her very eyes.

"Welcome to Urania Cottage, my dear. Read through these instructions. They should give you an idea of what's expected of you while you live under this roof."

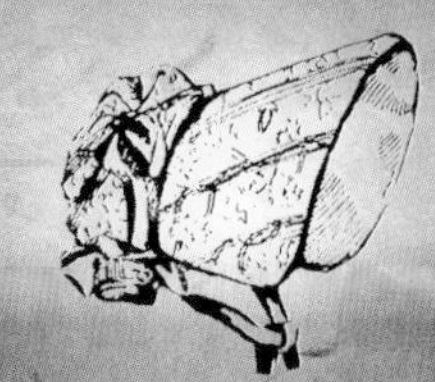

Urania Cottage closed in 1862. Fifty-six women came through its doors, and over half of them managed to turn their lives around. The remainder ran away or were expelled.

Urania Cottage: Timetable and Code of Conduct

The aim of Urania Cottage is to provide you with the correct skills and attitude to help you make a better life for yourself. Read through the following instructions carefully.

Daily Routine

6 am	*Rise, wash, dress and make your bed. Say your morning prayers. Residents will take it in turns to make breakfast. Breakfast will be eaten together.*
9 am	*Attend lessons in the parlour. These may include: reading, writing, arithmetic, needlework and music.*
noon	*Lunch will be served. Clear away your own dishes.*
1 pm	*Help with the housework. Residents will be expected to: wash bed linen, tend to the garden, sweep the floors or prepare dinner.*
6 pm	*Help serve dinner in the dining room.*
9 pm	*Return to your bedroom and say your prayers. Lamps will be extinguished at 10 pm.*

Expected Behaviour

- *Be polite, courteous and clean at all times.*
- *Guests are not permitted unless permission is granted by Matron.*
- *Any resident whose behaviour is unacceptable will be given a warning. Further bad behaviour will result in expulsion from Urania Cottage.*

A Tough Act to Follow

9TH FEBRUARY 1858 Charles glanced down at the row of eager, upturned faces. The stage lights were swelteringly hot, and Charles felt a trickle of sweat drip down the back of his neck. Once the rapturous applause had died down, Charles hunched his back, adopted a sneer and transformed himself into one of his most notorious characters: Ebenezer Scrooge. Striding into the centre of the stage he began.

"There's more of gravy than of grave about you, whatever you are!"

Charles embarked on several very successful reading tours during his lifetime, both in the UK and abroad. From 1867 to 1868, he undertook a reading tour in America, earning £19 000 (about £1.5 million in today's money).

The audience roared with laughter, clapping and cheering as he read passages from *A Christmas Carol*, bringing his characters to life before their eyes.

As the evening wore on, Charles hoped that the event had been a success. He'd volunteered to do the reading to raise funds for the Hospital for Sick Children. The hospital's wards were already bursting at the seams, and without financial support, there was a risk that it might close for good.

After the performance, Charles mingled with guests and well-wishers in the theatre's lobby. His friend, and the hospital's founder, Charles West, bounded towards him, grasped his hand and pumped it enthusiastically.

"Charles, my dear man! You are our saviour! I've just come from the ticket booth — the show was a sell-out! We think we've raised £3000 for the hospital!"

Charles beamed at him and clapped him on the back. "Who knew Ebenezer Scrooge could inspire so much generosity!"

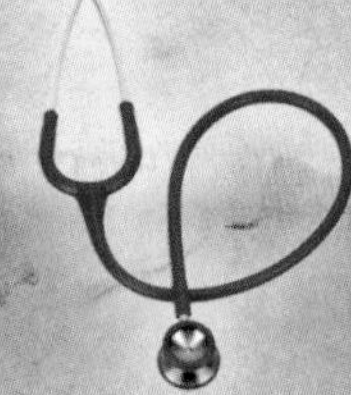

The money raised by Charles gave the hospital financial security and allowed them to buy another building next door. The 'Hospital for Sick Children' is now better known as 'Great Ormond Street Hospital'.

A Brush with Death

9TH JUNE 1865 The train whistled cheerfully as it chugged out of Folkestone station. Charles glanced down at his pocket watch and snapped it shut — 2.38 pm. Two minutes late — still, he should be back home for early evening. Although he travelled extensively due to his reading tours, nowhere could beat his beloved London.

The beautiful English countryside tore past his carriage window, and he admired a grand-looking **viaduct** up ahead. He peered a little closer. A tiny figure stood on the tracks waving a red flag. As they drew closer, Charles could see the panic and desperation written across his face. There was a screech of metal on metal as the driver slammed on the train's brakes, but it still lurched forward at a frightening speed. Charles's carriage jolted suddenly, and the floor beneath him twisted and buckled. Then came the sickening crunch of fragmenting wood. The yawning tension of bending metal. And the screams. Above all, the screams of people. Hurt people. Terrified people.

Charles tended to the injured passengers while he waited for help to arrive. When he was no longer needed, Charles retrieved his latest, unfinished novel, 'Our Mutual Friend', from the wreckage.

Charles got to his feet, staggering slightly as the floor creaked and tilted beneath him. He managed to squeeze out of a window. Before him lay destruction. Seven mangled, shattered and crumpled carriages lay in the ravine beneath the viaduct. An ashen-faced woman lay mere yards away from him, her leg bent unnaturally. Charles knelt by her side and her eyelids fluttered in response. He grasped her hand and whispered a story in her ear as she drifted out of consciousness.

Ten people were killed and dozens more were injured in the rail crash.

A Fond Farewell

FIVE YEARS TO THE DAY after the rail crash, Charles Dickens passed away. Friends and relatives said he never truly recovered from the incident.

Charles worked right up until his death. His final novel, *The Mystery of Edwin Drood*, was never finished, and Dickens fans still disagree about how it should end.

He was laid to rest in Westminster Abbey, in Poets' Corner — an area of the abbey where great British novelists, dramatists and poets are buried or commemorated. Every year, on the anniversary of his birth, a wreath is placed on his tomb.

What the Dickens!

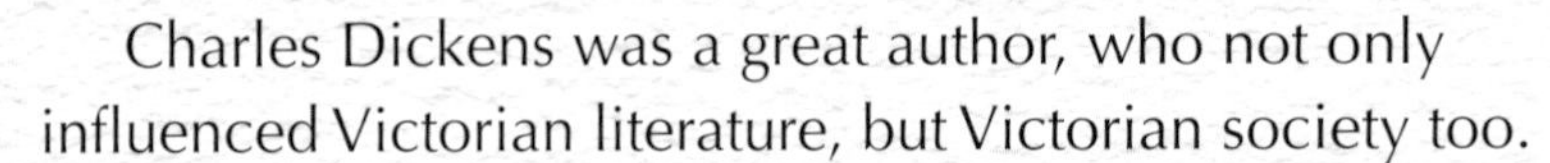

Charles Dickens was a great author, who not only influenced Victorian literature, but Victorian society too.

Victorian readership

Prior to the 19th century, literature and reading was confined to the rich — the poor couldn't afford to buy luxuries such as books, and many poor people couldn't read anyway. Dickens helped to make literature more accessible by publishing his stories in newspapers and magazines, which were much cheaper to buy — helping to reach a brand new audience.

Literary techniques

Writing serialised novels helped Dickens to change the style of Victorian literature. Because each episode usually ended with a cliffhanger, his novels had plenty of thrills and spills to keep readers coming back for more — Victorian novels were more exciting than ever before! Dickens worked hard to keep his stories interesting and engaging — he created almost 1000 named characters, and introduced about 250 new words to the English language (including 'butterfingers', 'cheesiness' and 'fluffiness').

Themes & social reform

Dickens brought some of Victorian society's biggest problems, such as poverty and injustice, to the attention of wealthy readers. This awareness helped to generate more support for the work of social reformers — people who worked towards improving the living and working conditions of Britain's poorest people.

Dickens's legacy

There have been over 200 film and TV adaptations of his work, and in 1960 *Oliver Twist* was made into the hit West End musical *Oliver!*, which has toured the globe. Between 1992 and 2003, the Bank of England celebrated Dickens's achievements by putting his face in the design of the £10 note.

Dickens's books have never gone out of print, and his novel *A Tale of Two Cities* is a best-seller, having sold over 200 million copies. There's no doubt that this popularity will continue for years to come.

Glossary

clerk — A person employed in an office who performs administrative tasks

consumption — An informal name for tuberculosis, a deadly lung disease

debtors' prison — A jail for people who owed money. Prison sentences generally lasted until the debt was paid off

ne'er-do-well — A lazy and irresponsible person

refuge — A safe, secure place

serialised novel — A story that was published in small sections over the course of months or years

viaduct — A bridge with several arches, usually carrying a railway or road across a valley

well-heeled — Wealthy

workhouse — A place where poor people were sent to live and work

Benjamin Zephaniah

"A radical poet"

written by Anna Hall

October 1993 Near the end of a long shift, Tim stood at the back of a small, musty club, struggling to stay awake. He could taste the lingering scent of old sweat in the air, and the plaster on the ceiling was peeling in places. Lazily, he reached out and flicked the switch to light up the stage for yet another dull act.

The performer wandered onto the stage with a casual swagger. He was only about average height, but he had a stage presence that filled the room. He moved with a relaxed ease that was fascinating, and yet there was still something mischievous about him. His name was Benjamin Zephaniah (Zeff-an-eye-a). Tim slowly followed the poet across the stage with the spotlight as he began to speak.

"Dis poetry is quick an childish
Dis poetry is fe de wise an foolish"

His accent was a unique blend of down-to-earth **Brummie** and exotic Jamaican, whilst the poetry's natural, **reggae** (regg-ay) rhythms were almost hypnotic. Even the rhymes seemed accidental. Tim was mesmerised. He forgot about the grimy club. He forgot how tired he was. He very nearly forgot to operate the spotlight.

This was unlike any other poetry Tim had ever heard. It was worlds away from the poems he'd learnt at school; this felt real and familiar. Zephaniah's poetry was made for the stage.

"This guy was born to perform," thought Tim.

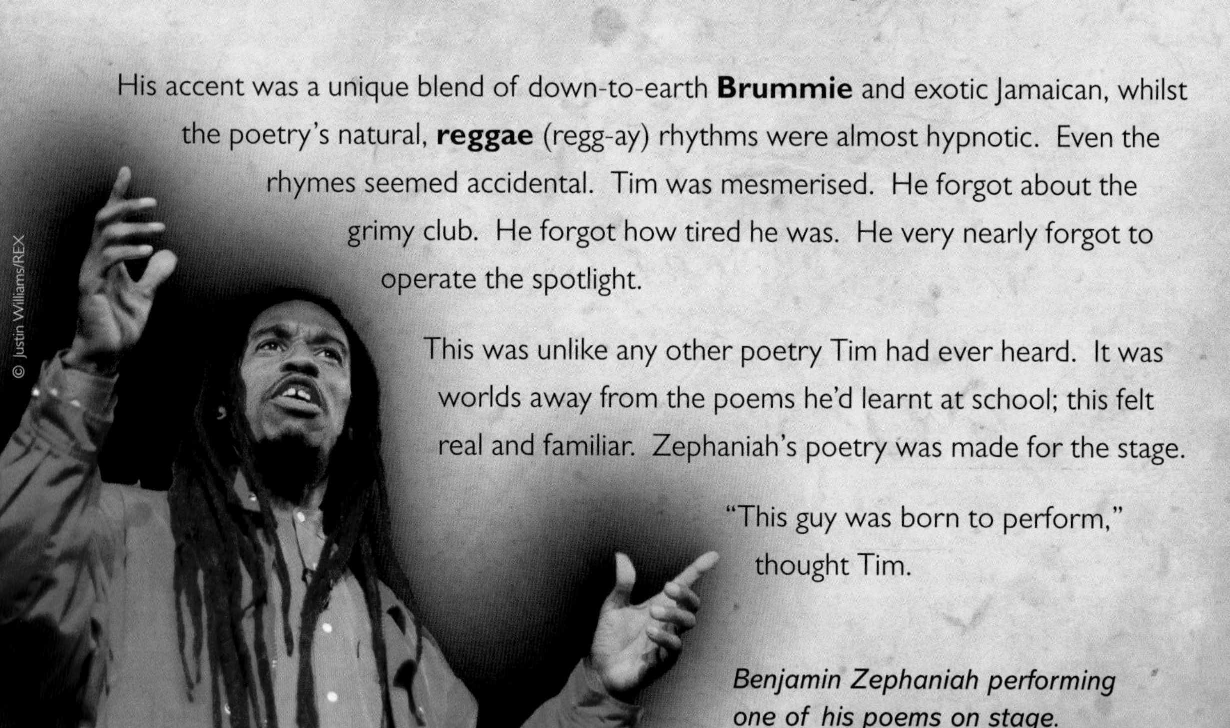

Benjamin Zephaniah performing one of his poems on stage.

The Boy from Birmingham

JUNE 1968 Ten-year-old Benjamin stood at the front of the church, his heart pounding and his hands clammy. He looked out at hundreds of expectant faces, as they waited for him to start reading from the huge Bible in front of him. But he couldn't give them the Bible reading they were expecting. Benjamin couldn't read.

Benjamin's mother travelled by boat from Jamaica to Britain in 1954. She settled in Handsworth, an area of Birmingham with a large Jamaican community. Benjamin was born in 1958 and was raised in Handsworth.

Suddenly, he had a flash of inspiration. Slowly he began to recite part of the Bible from memory. But he didn't just speak the words — he *performed* them. He spoke in rhythm as if he was keeping time with a beat that no one else could hear. Steadily, the rhythm of his chanting gained momentum and the beat intensified. Before he knew what was happening, Benjamin had worked the crowd up into a frenzy of applause. It was exhilarating — his first public performance had been a success!

AUGUST 1976 Benjamin felt a proud glow spreading across his face as he looked out at a different crowd. These people had come to watch him perform poetry. He had been making up poems in his head since he was eight, and now he was sharing his poetry with huge audiences like this one.

As he paced the stage, his eyes wandered over the faces in the audience. Each face was subtly different from the next and each told a different story. This was a real community, a diverse mix that reminded him of everything he loved about bustling and industrious Handsworth.

This was an energetic place that moved to an exotic beat. The audience in front of him was a melting pot of everything this vibrant area had to offer. This was home.

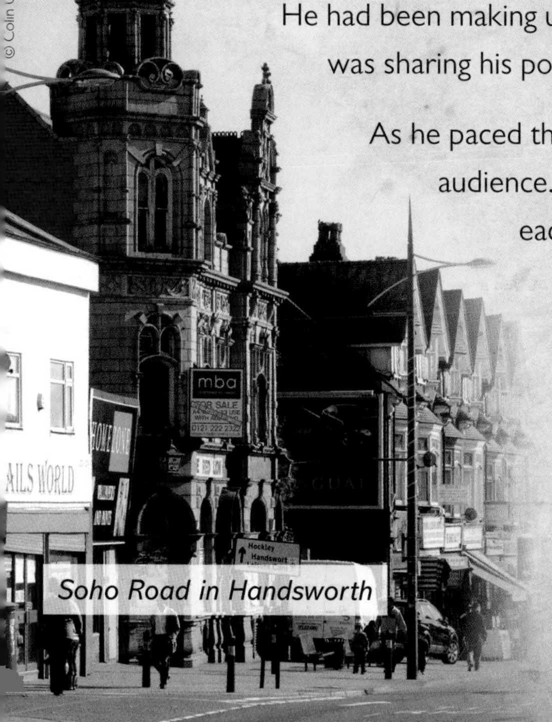

Soho Road in Handsworth

Small Beginnings

A year later, Benjamin sat at the kitchen table, staring into the distance. He was fuelling himself for another performance with an almost unbearably spicy bean curry. He needed a moment to catch his breath.

He was performing in packed clubs almost every night and had built up a devoted following across Birmingham. Over the last few years his fame had grown, and now it felt like his career as a dub poet was really taking shape.

What is Dub Poetry?

Where does it come from?

Dub poetry became popular in the 1970s in both Jamaica and England. At first, Jamaican artists played 'dub' versions of records and then performed raps over the top. (The 'dub' version only had the music from the song, without any words.) Initially these raps were made up on the spot, but eventually artists started writing them in advance and practising them. After a while, this style of performance became known as dub poetry.

What does it sound like?

Dub poetry is set to reggae rhythms. It is usually written in Jamaican patois (pat-wah), which is a Jamaican dialect based on the English language. This means that the words have a natural rhythm that makes the poetry sound musical even when it is performed without a drum beat. As a result, dub poetry often sounds like a form of chanting.

What are the poems about?

The musical sound of dub poetry is very absorbing. However, the poetry's content is also important. The poems usually deal with difficult issues like racism, but they may also contain lyrics celebrating music and poetry. They can be both serious and light-hearted.

Are the poems ever published?

Although dub poetry is sometimes found in print, it is usually performed. There are lots of dub poets performing across the country. Benjamin Zephaniah is probably the most well-known dub poet in the UK.

London Bound

OCTOBER 1980 Benjamin couldn't believe his eyes. He was looking at a printed book of his own poems. The title *Pen Rhythm* was boldly inscribed in large letters on the front cover, and underneath them was his name. His name!

Benjamin could still hear the voice of his teacher telling him he was a born failure. He had left school at thirteen unable to read or write. Determined to make a living from his poetry, he'd started performing in Birmingham. Two years ago, he had moved to London to spread his poems and his message to a wider audience.

At first it seemed impossible that he would ever overcome his problems with reading and writing, but in London he had gone to evening classes and he'd soon found out that he had **dyslexia**. He'd learnt to think in different ways so that this dyslexia didn't cause him so many problems. Now, this book would show the world that he could be a successful poet.

MAY 1981 Jason fought his way through the roaring crowd. He had never been to a protest before, and it was louder than he had expected. Shouts and cheers filled the air and the speakers boomed. Issues like unemployment, poor housing and racism were making people's lives difficult. This was a chance for everyone to make their voices heard.

Jason jumped up and caught a glimpse of the latest performer — Benjamin Zephaniah. He was dancing around the stage, performing against a backdrop of striking posters and banners. The hypnotic sound of his rhythmic poetry rose above the insistent bellowing of the crowd. His simple truths perfectly expressed the anger of the protest.

Jason turned to his friend and shouted, "This bloke's got what it takes. He really makes you think."

Benjamin moved to London in 1978, when he was 20.

A Lively Debate

TEN YEARS LATER Benjamin slowly sank into the warm depths of his favourite armchair. His whole body ached; in the last month, he had performed on every continent on the planet. But when he glanced down at his newspaper, his own name jumped off the page.

Broadham Chronicle

SATURDAY, FEBRUARY 2 1991 45P

PAGE VS. STAGE — YOU DECIDE

For years, the poetry taught in schools has been very traditional. However, the art of performance poetry is slowly making its way from the stage to the classroom.

Rudyard Kipling's poetry is often taught in schools.

Poetry on the Page

Some people believe that traditional poetry is superior to performance poetry because it offers a more rewarding challenge. It is designed to be read in peace and quiet. The reader can therefore take time to puzzle over longer sentences and more complicated techniques.

In addition, reading poetry requires more imagination. The reader cannot see the poet's gestures or hear his or her tone. As a result, the reader can interpret the meaning of the poem in their own way using only the words on the page.

Poetry on the Stage

On the other hand, Benjamin Zephaniah, one of Britain's best-known performance poets, argues that the most important thing about poetry is the way it *sounds*. For thousands of years, poetry was passed on verbally, and it is still devices like rhyme and rhythm that make poetry different from other forms of writing.

Furthermore, poetry on the stage is very lively and engaging. It is a good way of introducing poetry to people who wouldn't normally pick up a book of poems. The poems are often less formal and therefore less intimidating to people who are new to poetry.

Poetry on the page offers the reader an interesting challenge. However, poetry on the stage offers a new and exciting way to get into poetry. Is there a place for both in the classroom?

An Inspiring Performance

DECEMBER 1995 The children sat quietly at desks arranged in neat rows. Pegs attached the children's artwork to a string running from one corner of the room to another. Splashes of colour covered the light and airy classroom and the walls were covered with eye-catching displays.

'Talking Turkeys' was also the title of Benjamin's first book of poetry for children. It went straight to the top of the children's book charts and stayed there for months.

Memories of his schooldays came flooding back to Benjamin as he noticed that the children's bright red plastic chairs were the same as the ones he'd sat on as a boy. He tried to look each child in the eye as he performed his famous *Talking Turkeys* poem.

"Be nice to yu turkeys dis christmas
Cos turkeys just wanna hav fun"

Most of the children laughed wildly at the poem's hip-hop turkeys. Others listened with wrinkled foreheads and quizzical expressions. When he spoke the final line, the children clapped and cheered energetically. Many raised their hands, bursting with questions.

Benjamin's face lit up. The poems he'd studied at school had made him yawn and fidget, so when he had become a poet he'd been determined to do things differently. He wanted his words to inspire and excite young people. He'd even written about it in a poem called *Who's Who*.

"I used to think poets
Were boring,
Until I became one of them."

Benjamin wrote his poems to entertain as well as inform. Children loved them.

The cover of Benjamin's first book of poems for children.

A Letter from Afar

MARCH 1996 The envelope was crisp and white, with a handwritten address and a foreign stamp. Benjamin immediately recognised the careful swoop of the handwriting — this was a letter from Nelson Mandela! He tore it open and took in its contents. There was to be a concert in honour of Mandela at the splendid Royal Albert Hall, and he wanted Benjamin to co-host it alongside a South African poet.

Nelson Mandela lived in South Africa. He fought against the apartheid system of government in his country which forced people of different races to live apart and gave power to the small white population. Black people were treated as inferior citizens and weren't allowed to enter 'whites only' areas.

Memories flashed through Benjamin's head. He heard again the click of the letterbox as the first letter from Mandela was delivered. Mandela had heard Benjamin's *Free South Africa* track, and his letter was full of gratitude for Benjamin's work in fighting the brutality and injustice of apartheid (a-par-tie-d) in South Africa.

Nelson Mandela was imprisoned for 27 years for campaigning against apartheid, but he was released in 1990. He became President of South Africa in 1994.

Once again he felt the firm handshake of this courageous man as they met for the first time after Mandela's release from prison. He heard the roaring cheers of the crowd as they welcomed their hero to London. Then he saw a different crowd dancing gleefully across a television screen — this time in distant South Africa, where people were celebrating Mandela becoming president.

As he looked at this new letter, Benjamin sighed contentedly. He was passionate about the struggle against apartheid and Mandela was one of his idols. Now he would get a chance to share his respect for this great man at one of the most famous venues in the world. What would he say? Should it be serious or funny? Should he write a new poem?

A Night to Remember

11TH JULY 1996 Behind the stage of the Royal Albert Hall, Benjamin paced restlessly along a corridor lined with dressing-room doors. He could feel his pulse racing. He walked to the edge of the stage, dodging lights and cameras as he went, and peeked out from behind one of the heavy, velvet curtains. The luxurious red and gold interior of the Hall had the grandeur and scale of a palace. The impressive open space was surrounded by a series of circular galleries that seemed to be stacked on top of each other. They reached all the way up to the decorative round arches holding up the domed ceiling.

Benjamin listened as an expectant hush spread through the audience. He took a deep breath and stepped out into the blinding light.

TWO NATIONS CELEBRATE

AN EVENING IN HONOUR OF

NELSON MANDELA

The President of South Africa, Nelson Mandela, has arrived on UK soil. Who has achieved more in the field of human rights? Who else has had such a massive impact across the globe? Join the Queen and other dignitaries at a concert in his honour. Raise money for charity and enjoy a fantastic evening of entertainment.

The star-studded line up will feature diverse talents from both South Africa and the UK.

Phil Collins | **Bayete** | **Hugh Masekela** | **Benjamin Zephaniah**

Don't miss this unforgettable evening!

11th July 1996
Royal Albert Hall, London
Get your tickets now!

© Gallo images / Alamy

Strong Convictions

AUGUST 2001 The bulging shopping bags made a dull thud as Benjamin deposited them on the ancient wooden table in the middle of his homely kitchen. Shopping always took him a long time because he liked to read the labels on everything he bought; it was important to know what was in his food.

Half an hour later, the fragrant aroma of his favourite dish filled the steamy room. Benjamin was cooking one of his mother's recipes: a butter bean stew with potatoes. He tasted the sauce — perfect. It was full of flavour, with a tangy bite. People often asked Benjamin if vegan food made him feel weak. This question made him want to launch into an angry lecture — he was stronger, fitter and healthier than most people in their forties.

Benjamin is a vegan, so he doesn't eat any animal products. This includes meat, but also things like eggs and milk. He has written a lot of poetry about veganism, including 'The Little Book of Vegan Poems' in 2001.

SIX WEEKS LATER Benjamin sat back and rolled his shoulders to release some of the tension they were holding. He had just put the last full stop on the manuscript of his latest volume of poetry, entitled *Too Black, Too Strong*.

He frowned slightly as he read them once more. These poems contained a message he was determined to spread. They were about the struggles of black people in Britain and some of them were very critical of the government.

However, his features soon melted into a smile. These poems were really a celebration of free speech and **democracy** in Britain. In many other countries, he wouldn't have been able to write poems like these. Here, he was allowed to speak out, despite expressing views that probably weren't what the government wanted to hear.

Benjamin is well known for his strong views.

An Act of Defiance

The Queen awards OBEs to people who have achieved excellence in a particular area or made an outstanding contribution to the local community. Some people privately refuse the award before it is announced.

13TH NOVEMBER 2003 Benjamin scanned the very official-looking letter. It was from the office of Tony Blair, the Prime Minister, informing him that his name was being put forward as an Officer of the Order of the British Empire (OBE). His lips narrowed into a thin line and he glowered. He could feel his temperature rising as his eyes were drawn to the word 'empire'. Images of slavery and brutality leapt through his mind. The British Empire, which the award so proudly referred to, was an outrage. It had become rich through slavery. British ships had taken millions of Africans from their homes and transported them across the Atlantic Ocean to be sold. Benjamin only had to go back a few generations in his own family to find former slaves.

Suddenly he broke out into a chuckle. This was ridiculous! Whoever had come up with the idea had obviously never read any of his work. He had even written a whole poem, called *Bought and Sold*, about how greed for prizes and awards like this made poets too eager to please powerful people. It stopped them from writing poetry that challenged the world around them and instead made them write boring poems designed to please the people who gave out the awards.

"The lure of meeting royalty
And touching high society
Is damping creativity and eating at our heart."

Benjamin vowed that this would never happen to him. He didn't care about keeping important people happy. He was determined to keep writing about the issues that were important to him. He would have to publicly reject the OBE. Writing a newspaper article would allow him to explain his reasons.

An OBE is represented by a gold medal.

Echoes of the Past

The British Empire

At its peak, the British Empire was the largest empire in history. It was made up of territories ruled by the United Kingdom and it covered nearly a quarter of the globe.

All the areas in red were once part of the British Empire.

Rise and Fall The British Empire has its roots in the sixteenth century but reached its peak in the nineteenth century. By this time, Britain ruled over huge parts of the world, including India, Australia and large parts of Africa and the Caribbean. The people in these areas were controlled by governments made up of British settlers, who made laws and collected taxes. In the mid-twentieth century, the Empire declined sharply, with many countries gaining independence from British rule.

Development Projects The British built roads and railways in many of the territories in the Empire, in order to make it easier to take raw materials like tea and gold back to Britain. These transport links made travel and trade easier for local people once these countries became independent, which helped to boost the countries' economies.

Trade The British Empire opened up worldwide trade in goods like cotton and sugar, but Britain was also heavily involved in the slave trade. Slaves were bought in Africa and transported across the Atlantic to the Caribbean Islands. They were sold to landowners in exchange for raw materials like tobacco and rice. The British Empire made huge amounts of profit from the slave trade, while the slaves themselves endured terrible conditions and were forced to work for no money.

The Commonwealth Once they had gained independence, many of the countries that had been part of the Empire chose to join a voluntary organisation called the Commonwealth. Today, the Commonwealth still promotes trade between these countries and also encourages education, democracy and equality. It fights to reduce poverty and disease. Every four years, Commonwealth nations compete in a sporting event called the Commonwealth Games.

A Country Retreat

MAY 2009 Benjamin stepped outside and took a deep breath of fresh country air. He used the garden wall to do a few stretches and then broke into a swift jog down the stony path that ran along the side of his house and out into the open fields beyond. Benjamin drank in the beautiful scenery as his pulse rate began to rise and his muscles moved strongly beneath him.

Benjamin now splits his time between Lincolnshire and Beijing in China. He has various ways to relax, including restoring old English sportscars and playing or watching football (he is a lifelong Aston Villa fan).

Benjamin had moved to the small town of Spalding, in Lincolnshire, two years ago. He loved the rolling fields and open skies. It was another world compared to the bustling suburbs of Birmingham or the surging crowds of London, and it offered him an uninterrupted peace that was perfect for writing.

As he felt his heart rate increase, Benjamin pushed himself harder. He turned onto a new path and began a long incline. His muscles strained with the greater challenge and he focused his mind on reaching the top. As the path levelled off, he paused to recover and to take in the view — a marvellous **panorama** of the Lincolnshire countryside.

As soon as he got back to his bungalow, Benjamin began his **Tai Chi** (Tie-Chee) in the garden. He performed the routine calmly and slowly, focusing on the tranquillity of his surroundings. He concentrated on ridding his mind of any stressful thoughts that still remained after his run.

Once his heart had returned to its normal rhythm, Benjamin took a few deep breaths and then went inside. He would spend the morning writing. Hopefully he could turn some of the ideas he'd had during his run into some groundbreaking poetry, or maybe even a novel.

Investing in the Future

NOVEMBER 2009 Miss Perkins stood on Benjamin's doorstep. Her heart was beating wildly. She felt sick. What would she say to such an inspirational man? She straightened her skirt, took a deep breath and rang the doorbell. Before she could work herself up any more, Benjamin appeared at the door.

"Hello, I'm Miss Perkins," she began, the words tumbling from her mouth in an uncontrollable rush, "I teach at the High School. We've recently read one of your wonderful novels in class and I was wondering if you would consider coming in to perform for my students. They would really love to meet you."

To her surprise, Benjamin immediately agreed. He even invited her in. Miss Perkins stepped eagerly into the house, her nervousness slipping away as they spoke. He was like her — he wanted to excite children with writing that meant something to them.

Benjamin has written several novels for young people. They deal with challenging themes such as discrimination, violence and even murder.

Late in the afternoon, as she wandered home, Miss Perkins watched the sun slowly sink below the horizon. The man she had just met had been utterly charming, but he also had energy. He wanted to change things. Benjamin Zephaniah was a force to be reckoned with.

Glossary

Brummie — A nickname for something or someone from Birmingham

democracy — A type of government where people vote to elect a leader

dyslexia — A disorder that makes it difficult to read or spell

panorama — A wide view that extends in several different directions

reggae — A style of popular music originating from Jamaica in the 1960s

Tai Chi — A traditional Chinese form of exercise involving slow, calming movements